The Orchard Book of Nursery Rhymes

Daffy-down-dilly is new come to town,
With a yellow petticoat and a green gown.

The Orchard Book of
NURSERY RHYMES

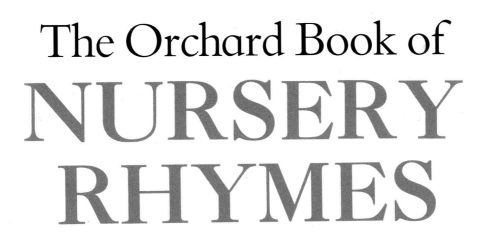

FAITH JAQUES

Rhymes chosen by Zena Sutherland

ORCHARD BOOKS

For Julian, Robin and Stephanie

ORCHARD BOOKS
338 Euston Road, London NW1 3BH
Orchard Books Australia
Level 17/207 Kent Street, Sydney, NSW 2000
First published in 1990 by Orchard Books
This collection © Zena Sutherland 1990
Illustrations © Faith Jaques 1990
Designed by Faith Jaques
ISBN 978 1 85213 056 5

The rights of Zena Sutherland to be identified as the compiler and of Faith Jaques
to be identified as the illustrator of this work have been asserted by them in accordance
with the Copyright, Designs and Patents Act, 1988.
A CIP catalogue record for this book is available from the British Library.
8 10 12 11 9 7
Printed in Malaysia
Orchard Books is a division of Hachette Children's Books,
an Hachette UK company.
www.hachette.co.uk

INTRODUCTION

Nursery rhymes are the perfect introduction to poetry. Even the very youngest child, who may not yet be able to walk or talk, can delight in the rhythm and rhyme, the exciting sounds of the language and, above all, in the sheer fun which make the rhymes immediately satisfying.

The richness of the language in this collection is given a new dimension by Faith Jaques's illustrations, which are a joy to look at. She has set the rhymes in the latter part of the eighteenth century, when they were first collected and published. The depth of her research and her unerring eye for detail bring a special quality to her work, giving children a visual experience that is both rewarding and absorbing.

Whether used as games, songs or pure poetry, nursery rhymes are part of the cultural heritage of every English speaking country. Children love them today, just as their parents and grandparents enjoyed them before. This familiarity makes them more receptive to remembering the rhymes, so ensuring that they will always be important links in the chain of oral tradition.

Zena Sutherland

Hush, little baby, don't say a word,
Papa's going to buy you a mocking bird.
If the mocking bird won't sing,
Papa's going to buy you a diamond ring.
If the diamond ring turns to brass,
Papa's going to buy you a looking-glass.
If the looking-glass gets broke,
Papa's going to buy you a billy-goat.
If that billy-goat runs away,
Papa's going to buy you another today.

Bye, baby bunting,
Daddy's gone a-hunting,
Gone to get a rabbit skin
To wrap the baby bunting in.

Rock-a-bye, baby, on the treetop,
When the wind blows, the cradle will rock;
When the bough breaks, the cradle will fall,
Down will come baby, cradle, and all.

This little pig went to market,
This little pig stayed at home,
This little pig had roast beef,
This little pig had none,
And this little pig cried, Wee-wee-wee-wee-wee,
I can't find my way home.

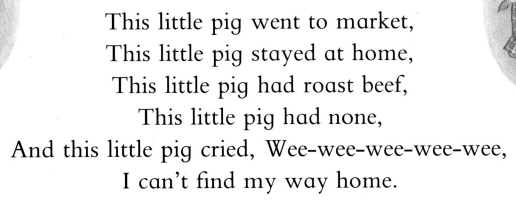

A was an apple pie.

B bit it.

C cut it.

D dealt it.

E eat it.

F fought for it.

G got it.

H had it.

I inspected it.

J jumped for it.

K kept it.

L longed for it.

M mourned for it.

P peeped in it.

N nodded at it.

Q quartered it.

O opened it.

R ran for it.

S stole it.

V viewed it.

T took it.

W wanted it.

U upset it.

X, Y, Z and ampersand,
All wished for a piece in hand.

Anna Elise,
She jumped with surprise;
The surprise was so quick,
It played her a trick;
The trick was so rare,
She jumped in a chair;
The chair was so frail,
She jumped in a pail;
The pail was so wet,
She jumped in a net;
The net was so small,
She jumped on a ball;
The ball was so round,
She jumped on the ground;
And ever since then
She's been turning around.

Hey! diddle, diddle,
The cat and the fiddle,
The cow jumped over the moon.
The little dog laughed
To see such sport,
And the dish ran away with the spoon.

Pat-a-cake, pat-a-cake, baker's man,
Bake me a cake as fast as you can.
Pat it and prick it and mark it with B,
Put it in the oven for baby and me.

Cock a doodle doo!
My dame has lost her shoe,
My master's lost his fiddling stick,
And knows not what to do.

One, two,
Buckle my shoe;

Three, four,
Knock at the door;

Five, six,
Pick up sticks;

Seven, eight,
Lay them straight;

Nine, ten,
A big fat hen;

Eleven, twelve,
Dig and delve;

Thirteen, fourteen,
Maids a-courting;

Fifteen, sixteen,
Maids in the kitchen;

Seventeen, eighteen,
Maids a-waiting;

Nineteen, twenty,
My plate's empty.

17

Boys and girls come out to play,
The moon doth shine as bright as day.
Leave your supper, and leave your sleep,
And join your playfellows in the street.
Come with a whoop, and come with a call,
Come with a good will or not at all.
Up the ladder and down the wall,
A half-penny loaf will serve us all.
You find milk, and I'll find flour,
And we'll have a pudding in half an hour.

In a cottage in Fife
Lived a man and his wife,
Who, believe me, were comical folk.
For, to people's surprise,
They both saw with their eyes,
And their tongues moved whenever they spoke.
When quite fast asleep,
I've been told that to keep
Their eyes open they could not contrive.
They walked on their feet,
And 'twas thought what they eat
Helped, with drinking, to keep them alive.

Pease porridge hot,
Pease porridge cold,
Pease porridge in the pot
Nine days old.
Some like it hot,
Some like it cold,
Some like it in the pot
Nine days old.

A diller, a dollar,
A ten o'clock scholar,
What makes you come so soon?
You used to come at ten o'clock
But now you come at noon.

Bow-wow, says the dog,
Mew, mew, says the cat,
Grunt, grunt, goes the hog,
And squeak goes the rat.
Tu-whu, says the owl,
Caw, caw, says the crow,
Quack, quack, says the duck,
What cuckoos say you know.

Hector Protector was dressed all in green;
Hector Protector was sent to the Queen.
The Queen did not like him,
No more did the King,
So Hector Protector was sent back again.

Yankee Doodle came to town,
Riding on a pony;
He stuck a feather in his cap,
And called it macaroni.

Gregory Griggs, Gregory Griggs
Had twenty-seven different wigs.
He wore them up, he wore them down,
To please the people of the town.
He wore them east, he wore them west,
But he never could tell which he loved the best.

Sing a song of sixpence,
A pocket full of rye;
Four and twenty blackbirds
Baked in a pie.

When the pie was opened,
The birds began to sing;
Wasn't that a dainty dish,
To set before the king?

The king was in his counting-house
Counting out his money;
The queen was in the parlour
Eating bread and honey.

The maid was in the garden
Hanging out the clothes,
When down came a blackbird
And pecked off her nose.

Pussy-cat, pussy-cat, where have you been?
I've been to London to look at the Queen.
Pussy-cat, pussy-cat, what did you there?
I frightened a little mouse under her chair.

Three blind mice, see how they run!
They all ran after the farmer's wife,
Who cut off their tails with the carving knife.
Did you ever see such a thing in your life,
As three blind mice?

Wee Willie Winkie runs through the town,
Upstairs and downstairs in his night-gown,
Rapping at the window, crying through the lock,
Are the children all in bed, for now it's eight o'clock?

Diddle, diddle, dumpling, my son John,
Went to bed with his trousers on;
One shoe off and one shoe on,
Diddle, diddle, dumpling, my son John.

Humpty Dumpty sat on a wall,
Humpty Dumpty had a great fall.
All the King's horses and all the King's men
Couldn't put Humpty together again.

Jack Sprat could eat no fat,
His wife could eat no lean;
And so, between them both, you see,
They licked the platter clean.

Georgie Porgie, pudding and pie,
Kissed the girls and made them cry.
When the boys came out to play,
Georgie Porgie ran away.

Peter, Peter, pumpkin eater,
Had a wife and couldn't keep her.
He put her in a pumpkin shell
And there he kept her very well.

The Queen of Hearts,
She made some tarts,
All on a summer's day.
The Knave of Hearts,
He stole those tarts,
And took them clean away.

The King of Hearts
Called for the tarts,
And beat the knave full sore.
The Knave of Hearts
Brought back the tarts,
And vowed he'd steal no more.

Little Tommy Tucker
Sings for his supper.
What shall we give him?
White bread and butter.
How shall he cut it
Without a knife?
How will he be married
Without a wife?

Little Polly Flinders
Sat among the cinders,
Warming her pretty little toes.
Her mother came and caught her,
And whipped her little daughter
For spoiling her nice new clothes.

Little Boy Blue,
Come blow your horn,
The sheep's in the meadow,
The cow's in the corn.
Where is the boy
Who looks after the sheep?
He's under a haycock
Fast asleep.
Will you wake him?
No, not I,
For, if I do,
He's sure to cry.

Little Miss Muffet
Sat on a tuffet,
Eating her curds and whey.
There came a big spider,
Who sat down beside her
And frightened Miss Muffet away.

Old King Cole
Was a merry old soul,
And a merry old soul was he.
He called for his pipe,
And he called for his bowl,
And he called for his fiddlers three.

Every fiddler he had a fiddle,
And a very fine fiddle had he.
Oh, there's none so rare,
As can compare,
With King Cole and his fiddlers three.

See-saw, Margery Daw,
Jacky shall have a new master.
Jacky shall have but a penny a day
Because he can't work any faster.

Mary, Mary, quite contrary,
How does your garden grow?
With silver bells and cockle shells,
And pretty maids all in a row.

Little Bo-peep has lost her sheep,
And doesn't know where to find them.
Leave them alone, and they'll come home,
Bringing their tails behind them.

Little Bo-peep fell fast asleep,
And dreamt she heard them bleating.
But when she awoke, she found it a joke,
For they were still a-fleeting.

Then up she took her little crook,
Determined for to find them.
She found them indeed, but it made her heart bleed,
For they'd left their tails behind them.

It happened one day, as Bo-peep did stray
Into a meadow hard by,
There she espied their tails side by side,
All hung on a tree to dry.

She heaved a sigh, and wiped her eye,
And over the hillocks went rambling,
And tried what she could, as a shepherdess should,
To tack again each to its lambkin.

There was an old woman who lived in a shoe,
She had so many children she didn't know what to do.
She gave them some broth without any bread;
She whipped them all soundly and put them to bed.

Simple Simon met a pieman
Going to the fair.
Says Simple Simon to the pieman,
Let me taste your ware.

Says the pieman to Simple Simon,
Show me first your penny.
Says Simple Simon to the pieman,
Indeed I have not any.

Ding, dong, bell,
Pussy's in the well!
Who put her in?
Little Johnny Green.
Who pulled her out?
Little Tommy Stout.
What a naughty boy was that
To try to drown poor pussy cat,
Who never did him any harm,
And killed the mice in his father's barn.

Tom, Tom, the piper's son,
Stole a pig and away he run.
The pig was eat,
And Tom was beat,
And Tom went howling down the street.

Ring-a-ring o' roses,
A pocket full of posies,
A-tishoo! A-tishoo!
We all fall down.

The cows are in the meadow,
Lying fast asleep,
A-tishoo! A-tishoo!
We all get up again.

Jack and Jill
Went up the hill,
To fetch a pail of water.
Jack fell down,
And broke his crown,
And Jill came tumbling after.

Baa, baa, black sheep,
Have you any wool?
Yes, sir, yes, sir,
Three bags full.
One for the master,
And one for the dame,
And one for the little boy
Who lives down the lane.

Mary had a little lamb,
Its fleece was white as snow,
And everywhere that Mary went,
The lamb was sure to go.

It followed her to school one day,
That was against the rule.
It made the children laugh and play
To see a lamb at school.

And so the teacher turned it out,
But still it lingered near
And waited patiently about,
Till Mary did appear.

Why does the lamb love Mary so?
The eager children cry;
Why, Mary loves the lamb, you know,
The teacher did reply.

Bobby Shaftoe's gone to sea,
Silver buckles at his knee.
He'll come back and marry me,
Bonny Bobby Shaftoe!

Bobby Shaftoe's bright and fair,
Combing down his yellow hair.
He's my ain for evermair,
Bonny Bobby Shaftoe!

Polly put the kettle on,
Polly put the kettle on,
Polly put the kettle on,
We'll all have tea.

Sukey take it off again,
Sukey take it off again,
Sukey take it off again,
They've all gone away.

Goosey, goosey gander,
Whither shall I wander?
Upstairs and downstairs,
And in my lady's chamber.
There I met an old man,
Who would not say his prayers,
I took him by the left leg
And threw him down the stairs.

I had a little nut tree,
Nothing would it bear
But a silver nutmeg
And a golden pear.
The King of Spain's daughter
Came to visit me,
And all for the sake
Of my little nut tree.

Little Jack Horner
Sat in the corner,
Eating his Christmas pie.
He put in his thumb,
And pulled out a plum,
And said, What a good boy am I!

Old Mother Hubbard
Went to the cupboard,
To fetch her poor dog a bone;
But when she got there
The cupboard was bare,
And so the poor dog had none.

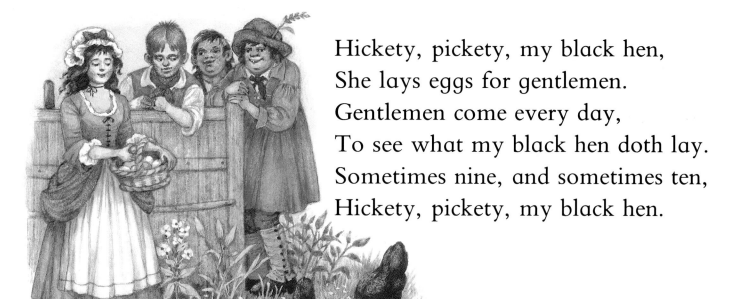

Hickety, pickety, my black hen,
She lays eggs for gentlemen.
Gentlemen come every day,
To see what my black hen doth lay.
Sometimes nine, and sometimes ten,
Hickety, pickety, my black hen.

Hickory, dickory, dock,
The mouse ran up the clock.
The clock struck one,
The mouse ran down,
Hickory, dickory, dock.

I saw a ship a-sailing,
A-sailing on the sea,
And oh, but it was laden
With pretty things for thee.

There were comfits in the cabin,
And apples in the hold.
The sails were made of silk,
And the masts were all of gold.

The four-and-twenty sailors,
That stood between the decks,
Were four-and-twenty white mice
With chains about their necks.

The captain was a duck
With a packet on his back,
And when the ship began to move
The captain said, Quack! Quack!

This is the house that Jack built.

This is the malt,
That lay in the house that Jack built.

This is the rat,
That ate the malt,
That lay in the house that Jack built.

This is the cat,
That killed the rat,
That ate the malt,
That lay in the house that Jack built.

50

This is the dog,
That worried the cat,
That killed the rat,
That ate the malt,
That lay in the house that Jack built.

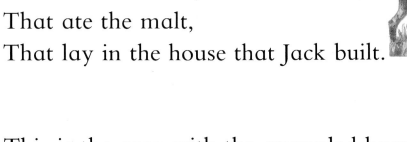

This is the cow with the crumpled horn,
That tossed the dog,
That worried the cat,
That killed the rat,
That ate the malt,
That lay in the house that Jack built.

This is the maiden all forlorn,
That milked the cow with the crumpled horn,
That tossed the dog,
That worried the cat,
That killed the rat,
That ate the malt,
That lay in the house that Jack built.

This is the man all tattered and torn,
That kissed the maiden all forlorn,
That milked the cow with the crumpled horn,
That tossed the dog,
That worried the cat,
That killed the rat,
That ate the malt,
That lay in the house that Jack built.

This is the priest all shaven and shorn,
That married the man all tattered and torn,
That kissed the maiden all forlorn,
That milked the cow with the crumpled horn,
That tossed the dog,
That worried the cat,
That killed the rat,
That ate the malt,
That lay in the house that Jack built.

This is the cock that crowed in the morn,
That waked the priest all shaven and shorn,
That married the man all tattered and torn,
That kissed the maiden all forlorn,
That milked the cow with the crumpled horn,
That tossed the dog,
That worried the cat,
That killed the rat,
That ate the malt,
That lay in the house that Jack built.

This is the farmer sowing his corn,
That kept the cock that crowed in the morn,
That waked the priest all shaven and shorn,
That married the man all tattered and torn,
That kissed the maiden all forlorn,
That milked the cow with the crumpled horn,
That tossed the dog,
That worried the cat,
That killed the rat,
That ate the malt,
That lay in the house that Jack built.

Three little kittens, they lost their mittens,
And they began to cry,
Oh, mother dear, we sadly fear
That we have lost our mittens.
What! lost your mittens, you naughty kittens!
Then you shall have no pie.
Mee-ow, mee-ow, mee-ow,
No, you shall have no pie.

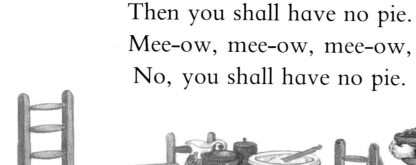

The three little kittens, they found their mittens,
And they began to cry,
Oh, mother dear, see here, see here,
For we have found our mittens.
Put on your mittens, you silly kittens,
And you shall have some pie.
Purr-r, purr-r, purr-r,
Oh, let us have some pie.

The three little kittens put on their mittens,
And soon ate up the pie.
Oh, mother dear, we greatly fear
That we have soiled our mittens.
What! soiled your mittens, you naughty kittens!
Then they began to sigh.
Mee-ow, mee-ow, mee-ow,
Then they began to sigh.

The three little kittens they washed their mittens.
And hung them out to dry.
Oh! mother dear, do you not hear
That we have washed our mittens?
What! washed your mittens, then you're good kittens,
But I smell a rat close by.
Mee-ow, mee-ow, mee-ow,
We smell a rat close by.

Higglety, pigglety, pop!
The dog has eaten the mop.
The pig's in a hurry,
The cat's in a flurry,
Higglety, pigglety, pop!

There was a maid on Scrabble Hill,
And if not dead, she lives there still.
She grew so tall, she reached the sky,
And on the moon hung clothes to dry.

Three young rats with black felt hats,
Three young ducks with white straw flats,
Three young dogs with curling tails,
Three young cats with demi-veils,
Went out to walk with three young pigs
In satin vests and sorrel wigs.
But suddenly it chanced to rain,
And so they all went home again.

I do not like thee, Doctor Fell,
The reason why I cannot tell.
But this I know, and know full well,
I do not like thee, Doctor Fell.

There was a young farmer of Leeds,
Who swallowed six packets of seeds.
It soon came to pass
He was covered with grass,
And he couldn't sit down for the weeds.

Doctor Foster went to Gloucester
In a shower of rain.
He stepped in a puddle,
Right up to his middle,
And never went there again.

Peter Piper picked a peck of pickled pepper;
A peck of pickled pepper Peter Piper picked.
If Peter Piper picked a peck of pickled pepper,
Where's the peck of pickled pepper Peter Piper picked?

How much wood would a woodchuck chuck,
If a woodchuck could chuck wood?
He would chuck as much wood
As a woodchuck could chuck,
If a woodchuck could chuck wood.

Moses supposes his toeses are roses,
But Moses supposes erroneously,
For nobody's toeses are posies of roses,
As Moses supposes his toeses to be.

Betty Botter bought some butter,
But, she said, the butter's bitter;
If I put it in my batter
It will make my batter bitter.
But a bit of better butter,
Will make my batter better.
So she bought a bit of butter,
Better than her bitter butter,
And she put it in her batter
And the batter was not bitter.
So t'was better Betty Botter
Bought a bit of better butter.

Monday's child is
fair of face,

Tuesday's child is
full of grace,

Wednesday's child is
full of woe,

Thursday's child has
far to go,

Friday's child is
loving and giving,

Saturday's child works
hard for his living,

But the child that's born on the Sabbath day
Is bonny and blithe and good and gay.

Jack be nimble,
Jack be quick,
Jack jump over
The candlestick.

Ride a cock-horse to Banbury Cross,
To see a fine lady upon a white horse.
Rings on her fingers and bells on her toes,
She shall have music wherever she goes.

There was a crooked man
And he walked a crooked mile,
He found a crooked sixpence
Against a crooked stile.
He bought a crooked cat
Which caught a crooked mouse,
And they all lived together
In a little crooked house.

One misty, moisty morning,
When cloudy was the weather,
I met a little old man,
Clothed all in leather.

He began to compliment
And I began to grin,
How do you do and how do you do
And how do you do again?

Flying-man, Flying-man,
Up in the sky,
Where are you going to,
Flying so high?

Over the mountains
And over the sea,
Flying-man, Flying-man,
Can't you take me?

There was an old woman tossed up in a basket,
Seventeen times as high as the moon.
Where she was going I couldn't but ask it,
For in her hand she carried a broom.

Old woman, old woman, old woman, quoth I,
Where are you going to up so high?
To brush the cobwebs off the sky!
May I go with you? Aye, by-and-by.

Here we go round the mulberry bush,
The mulberry bush, the mulberry bush.
Here we go round the mulberry bush,
On a cold and frosty morning.

This is the way we wash our hands,
Wash our hands, wash our hands.
This is the way we wash our hands,
On a cold and frosty morning.

This is the way we wash our clothes,
Wash our clothes, wash our clothes.
This is the way we wash our clothes,
On a cold and frosty morning.

This is the way we go to school,
Go to school, go to school.
This is the way we go to school,
On a cold and frosty morning.

This is the way we come out of school,
Come out of school, come out of school.
This is the way we come out of school,
On a cold and frosty morning.

The north wind doth blow,
And we shall have snow,
And what will poor Robin do then,
Poor thing?
He'll sit in a barn,
And keep himself warm,
And hide his head under his wing,
Poor thing.

Christmas is coming,
The geese are getting fat,
Please to put a penny
In the old man's hat.
If you haven't got a penny,
A ha'penny will do.
If you haven't got a ha'penny,
Then God bless you!

The first day of Christmas,
My true love sent to me,
A partridge in a pear tree.

The second day of Christmas,
My true love sent to me,
Two turtle doves, and
A partridge in a pear tree.

The third day of Christmas,
My true love sent to me,
Three French hens,
Two turtle doves, and
A partridge in a pear tree.

The fourth day of Christmas,
My true love sent to me,
Four colly birds,
Three French hens,
Two turtle doves, and
A partridge in a pear tree.

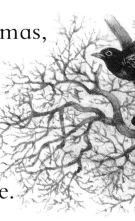

The fifth day of Christmas,
My true love sent to me,
Five gold rings,
Four colly birds,
Three French hens,
Two turtle doves, and
A partridge in a pear tree.

The sixth day of Christmas,
My true love sent to me,
Six geese a-laying,
Five gold rings,
Four colly birds,
Three French hens,
Two turtle doves, and
A partridge in a pear tree.

The seventh day of Christmas,
My true love sent to me,
Seven swans a-swimming,
Six geese a-laying,
Five gold rings,
Four colly birds,
Three French hens,
Two turtle doves, and
A partridge in a pear tree.

The eighth day of Christmas,
My true love sent to me,
Eight maids a-milking,
Seven swans a-swimming,
Six geese a-laying,
Five gold rings,
Four colly birds,
Three French hens,
Two turtle doves, and
A partridge in a pear tree.

The ninth day of Christmas,
My true love sent to me,
Nine drummers drumming,
Eight maids a-milking,
Seven swans a-swimming,
Six geese a-laying,
Five gold rings,
Four colly birds,
Three French hens,
Two turtle doves, and
A partridge in a pear tree.

The tenth day of Christmas,
My true love sent to me,
Ten pipers piping,
Nine drummers drumming,
Eight maids a-milking,
Seven swans a-swimming,
Six geese a-laying,
Five gold rings,
Four colly birds,
Three French hens,
Two turtle doves, and
A partridge in a pear tree.

The eleventh day of Christmas,
My true love sent to me,
Eleven ladies dancing,
Ten pipers piping,
Nine drummers drumming,
Eight maids a-milking,
Seven swans a-swimming,
Six geese a-laying,
Five gold rings,
Four colly birds,
Three French hens,
Two turtle doves, and
A partridge in a pear tree.

The twelfth day of Christmas,
My true love sent to me,
Twelve lords a-leaping,
Eleven ladies dancing,
Ten pipers piping,
Nine drummers drumming,
Eight maids a-milking,
Seven swans a-swimming,
Six geese a-laying,
Five gold rings,
Four colly birds,
Three French hens,
Two turtle doves, and
A partridge in a pear tree.

FAITH JAQUES WRITES ABOUT THE RHYMES

The nursery rhymes in this collection are mainly set in rural England towards the end of the eighteenth century. Although many of the rhymes originate much earlier and some may even go back to the Middle Ages and before, they had always been handed on by word of mouth, and it was only in the 1780s that books containing collections of nursery rhymes began to be published.

This seemed a good reason to set the illustrations in this period. The eighteenth century is an attractive period to illustrate, and everything in the pictures – clothes, houses, domestic detail, gardens – is of that time or earlier.

I have based the street scenes on real towns and villages depicted in paintings and engravings, but there are two rhymes set in specific places where it seemed important to show the actual locations. One of them is *I do not like thee, Doctor Fell* (p. 60), which is set in Oxford. Dr Fell was a much-disliked Dean of Christ Church and I have therefore

shown Christ Church in the background. The other rhyme is *Doctor Foster went to Gloucester* (p. 61). I have chosen to illustrate New Inn, a well-known coaching inn which (I believe) is still standing in the city of Gloucester today.

There is one rhyme, *Hush, little baby, don't say a word* (p. 7), which is set in the southern states of the United States. I wanted to make this clear, so I looked for trees which were typical of the area. The picture shows dogwood at the top and cottonwood at the bottom, with magnolia on the left and a tulip tree on the right.

Details of decoration, furniture, utensils and domestic scenes are based on contemporary sources. I have also tried to keep the colours right, to the soft pinks, lilacs, blues and greens so distinctive of the Georgian period.

The twenty-four little pictures in *A was an apple pie* (p. 10) each have a different setting and indeed a different apple pie! I have tried to spread the social mix as much as I could; some of the characters live in splendid eighteenth-century houses and others live in cottages. The furniture and wallpapers are typical of the period, and in 'L longed for it' the beginning of the Chinese influence is seen in the porcelain vase. In the last picture (p.13) I have shown an ampersand so that children will know what one looks like.

Betty Botter bought some butter (p. 63) shows a kitchen of the period. The utensils were carefully researched. Betty herself is a somewhat messy cook! Sugar would be bought as a tall hard cone, mounted on a wooden base. Special cutters were used to cut off a piece at the top which was then flattened back to granular form on a piece of paper with a knife. Flour for daily use was stored in tight-lidded wooden boxes. Cooking pots were made of cast iron, baking dishes of tin or earthenware. Although poor families usually ate off wooden or earthenware platters and bowls, most could afford a china jug, and pewter plates were not uncommon.

In *Three little kittens* (p.54) there are more utensils and cooking pots; in fact, the rolling pin is very like the ones we use today. The blue and white striped dishes we use today were also found in eighteenth-century kitchens. Water was heated over the kitchen fire and as there was no point in heating up small quantities, kettles were always very large like the one in *Polly put in the kettle on* (p. 44).

Pease porridge hot (p. 20) is set in a typical farm kitchen. The pease porridge (a kind of thick soup made from dried or split peas) has been cooked for a very long time in the pot, which is now on the table. The cooking pot would have been suspended over the fire with a chain and hook.

The cake in *Pat-a-cake, pat-a-cake, baker's man* (p. 16) was cooked by the village baker in his oven – a useful arrangement as villagers who had no oven could have their prepared loaves, pies and cakes cooked by the baker for a small sum of money.

Children at this time were quite often badly treated. *Little Polly Flinders* (p.30) is an example of how frequently people seemed to whip their children. There are several old engravings showing mothers or fathers wielding a bundle of birch twigs over a child. The twigs were often hung up on the kitchen wall ready to use.

The domestic animals I have included in the pictures are authentic breeds of the period. The pig was the all-purpose animal kept in villages and it could feed a family for a very long time – no wonder so many rhymes mention them. The piglet in *Higglety, pigglety, pop!* (p.58) is a Gloucester Old Spot and was much more hairy than pigs are today. Less hairy pigs were also quite common, but they were much larger and fatter than the pigs we breed now.

The Dalmatian in *Bow-wow, says the dog* (p. 21) was a fashionable dog for the rich, often trained to run underneath carriages. It was regarded as an elegant accessory to one's outfit. The dogs in *Ding, dong, bell* (p. 38) are mongrels, and the one in *The house that Jack built* (p. 50) is a whippet – a useful dog in the country for catching rats and rabbits.

Another interesting animal is the woodchuck in the American rhyme *How much wood would a woodchuck chuck* (p. 62). The woodchuck is a Northeast American member of the marmot family, and the name comes from the Cree Indian word 'wuchak'. It can be quite a pest and will eat garden vegetables and flowers, but it is not at all interested in wood.

One of the pleasures of illustrating the eighteenth century is the richness and variety of the costumes, and indeed the wealth of social history to be found in what people wore.

Gregory Griggs (p. 23) is a favourite rhyme and I seized the chance to show twenty-seven different wigs. The little pictures roughly go through the century from about 1730 in the first picture, then show a range of wigs to the end of the century. Although each wig is different, at that time dress changed quite slowly.

Clothes were expensive, so even if you were well-to-do you made them last. They were well made, of good quality cloth. Poorer people made their own, or bought old second-hand clothes.

Hector Protector (p. 22) is another favourite rhyme. I have made him a dandy with a high wig, patches on his face and a frilly cravat. He probably wore corsets too and padded his calves to produce a shapely leg.

In *Georgie Porgie, pudding and pie* (p. 28) the children are all from well-off families. Georgian colours were soft and muted but portraits of the time show that small boys were frequently dressed in bright scarlet jackets. You can see this again in *Little Jack Horner* (p. 46). Under the age of five, children wore dresses. The baby in *Moses supposes his toeses are roses* (p. 62) could be a boy or a girl.

Bobby Shaftoe (p. 44) is around thirteen years old and a cabin boy setting off to sea for the first time. He wears a reefer jacket and striped breeches – older sailors wore striped loose trousers at this time. His wrinkled stockings show his ineptitude at putting on his new clothes.

Hats were an important part of dress for the period. Men always wore them out of doors, women's hair was always covered by a white muslin cap and poorer women wore a straw hat over the cap. Rich ladies wore large hats over their wigs. In *Three young rats with black felt hats* (p. 59) I have dressed the animals in their best clothes for their walk, all wearing hats except the pigs. I feel that the ducks' 'white straw flats' must mean hats. These were an almost flat circle of straw, with hardly any crown; the ribbon was threaded through so that it came down the outside of the brim to give the hat a particular shape.

There were many fashions in shoes for the upper classes. The shoe in *There was an old woman who lived in a shoe* (p. 36) is made of embroidered brocade and typical of the decorative shoes of the period. Men's shoes were generally black with buckles or big bows.

The costumes in *The first day of Christmas* (p. 74) are very French. Many sources say that this rhyme was originally a French carol, maybe of the medieval period or even earlier. I have set it on a large estate in rural France. French clothes became very exotic after the Revolution in 1789: the hats were enormous and worn either on top of wigs or on natural hair fuzzed up to make it look bulky. Stripes were fashionable and nearly everything was striped in different widths and different directions. French fashion was based on the sophistication of the town; English fashion was based on country clothes and was much plainer, except for very formal town occasions.

I thoroughly enjoyed researching the origins of the rhymes. For this I must acknowledge the scholarship of Iona and Peter Opie, whose *Oxford Dictionary of Nursery Rhymes* was one of my main sources. I also tried hard to discover the meaning of words and expressions which are now used in quite another sense. For instance, the word 'dollar' used in *A diller, a dollar* (p. 20) was once Cockney rhyming slang for 'Oxford Scholar'.

The origins of nursery rhymes make fascinating reading but they are not always conclusive.

There are all kinds of suggestions about the origin of *Humpty Dumpty* (p. 27). It has been said he was King Richard III, reputed to be hunch-backed, but this is doubtful. He is always depicted as an egg, perhaps the best example of something you really can't put together again once it's broken! Humpty Dumpty was also at one time a term used for someone small and fat.

There are other examples of nicknames given to poor unfortunates who didn't measure up to what was normal for the time. *Jack Sprat* (p. 27) was the term given to dwarfs and 'Simon' of *Simple Simon* (p. 37) was the term used for a simpleton. The village idiot might be called Simon even though he had been christened John!

Often, too, the meaning of nursery rhymes has become distorted. In recent years illustrations of *Tom, Tom, the piper's son* (p. 39) usually show Tom with a real pig (physically impossible) or piglet under his arm. In fact, the 'pig' refers to a pastry pig. Poor people tended to buy from street vendors and this particular vendor has a basket filled with pastry pigs containing mincemeat. I am not sure whether this would have been savoury minced meat or sweet mincemeat.

Another example of a possibly distorted meaning is in *Cock a doodle doo!* (p. 16). The 'master' is usually thought to be the dame's husband, but I believe he is the dancing master who was an important part of every upper-class household. Dancing at that time was very formal and highly organised, and everyone needed tuition. Engravings of the period, such as Hogarth's *The Rake's Progress*, show the dancing master with a tiny violin and bow, presumably so that he wouldn't be too cluttered up while he taught the steps of the dance.

Here we go round the mulberry bush (p. 70) is well-known as a song with a memorable catchy tune. This rhyme was rather perplexing to illustrate since the mulberry is a tree, not a bush. So I had to make the tree small and bushy. One source suggests that the mulberry was traditionally the tree planted in prison yards, and that prisoners walked around it for their daily exercise.

Almost every rhyme has a story to tell, or can illuminate some aspect of life in the past. There is not the space to expand on this theme here, but the Opies' *Oxford Dictionary of Nursery Rhymes* is invaluable and anyone interested in knowing more will see how their comments are the springboard to my illustrations.

INDEX OF FIRST LINES